NorthParadePublishing

©2014 North Parade Publishing Ltd.
4 North Parade,
Bath BA1 1LF. UK
www.nppbooks.co.uk

My Favourite

Nursery
Rhymes

A charming collection of traditional
nursery rhymes, with full colour
illustrations by Gaby Hanson

The Queen of Hearts,
  She made some tarts,
All on a summer's day.
The Knave of Hearts,
He stole the tarts,
And took them clean away.

The King of Hearts,
  Called for the tarts,
And scolded the knave full sore.
The Knave of Hearts,
Brought back the tarts,
And vowed he'd steal no more.

Little Miss Muffet
Sat on a tuffet,
Eating her curds and whey;
There came a big spider,
And sat down beside her,
And frightened Miss Muffet away.

Three little kittens,
    they lost their mittens,
And they began to cry,
"Oh, Mother, dear, we sadly fear,
    Our mittens we have lost."
"What! Lost your mittens?
    You naughty kittens,
Then you shall have no pie.
    Meow, meow,
Then you shall have no pie."

The three little kittens,
    they found their mittens,
And they began to cry,
"Oh, Mother, dear, see here, see here,
    Our mittens we have found."
"What! Found your mittens?
Then you're good kittens,
And you shall have some pie.
Purr, purr,
Then you shall have some pie."

The three little kittens,
　　　　put on their mittens,
　　And soon ate up the pie.
"Oh, Mother, dear, we sadly fear,
　　Our mittens we have soiled."
What! Soiled your mittens?
　　You naughty kittens".
And they began to sigh.
　　"Meow, meow,"
And they began to sigh.
The three little kittens,
　　　　they washed their mittens,
　　And hung them out to dry.

Humpty Dumpty sat on a wall;
Humpty Dumpty had a great fall.
  All the King's horses
  And all the King's men
Couldn't put Humpty together again!

Little Betty Blue
Lost her holiday shoe;
What shall little Betty do?

Give her another
    To match the other
And then she'll walk upon two.

I love little pussy,
Her coat is so warm;
And if I don't hurt her,
She'll do me no harm.
So I'll not pull her tail,
Nor drive her away;
But pussy and I
Very gently will play.

I'll pat little pussy,
And then she will purr;
And thus show her thanks for
My kindness to her.
I'll not pinch her ears,
Nor tread on her paws;
Lest it should provoke her
To use her sharp claws!

She shall sit by my side,
And I'll give her some food;
And pussy will love me
Because I am good.

L ittle Jack Horner
Sat in a corner,
    Eating a mincemeat pie.
He stuck in his thumb
And pulled out a plum,
    And said, "What a good boy am I!"

Jack and Jill went up the hill
  To fetch a pail of water
Jack fell down and broke his crown
And Jill came tumbling after.

Up got Jack, and home did trot
As fast as he could caper
He went to bed and bound his head
With vinegar and brown paper.

H ey Diddle Diddle
The cat and the fiddle,
The cow jumped over the moon.
The little dog laughed to see such fun,
And the dish ran away with the spoon!

One, two,
Buckle my shoe;

Three, four,
Shut the door;

Five, six,
Pick up sticks;

Seven, eight,
Lay them straight;

Nine, ten,
A good, fat hen;

Eleven, twelve,
Dig and delve;

Thirteen, fourteen,
Maids a-courting;

Fifteen, sixteen,
Maids in the kitchen;

Seventeen, eighteen,
Maids a-waiting;

Nineteen, twenty,
My plate's empty.

Hush-a-bye, baby, on the tree top!
When the wind blows the cradle will rock;
When the bough breaks the cradle will fall;
Down will come baby, cradle and all.

Rock-a-bye, baby, thy cradle is green;
Father's a nobleman, Mother's a queen;
Sister's a lady, who wears a gold ring;
And Brother's a drummer, who plays for the king.

Hush-a-bye, baby, way up on high;
Never mind, baby, Mummy is nigh;
Swinging the baby all around –
Hush-a-bye, baby, up hill and down.

Sing a song of sixpence,
A pocket full of rye;
Four and twenty blackbirds
  Baked in a pie.
When the pie was opened,
  The birds began to sing;
Wasn't that a dainty dish
  To set before the king?

The King was in his counting house,
  Counting out his money;
The Queen was in the parlour
  Eating bread and honey.
The maid was in the garden,
  Hanging out the clothes;
When along came a blackbird
  And pecked off her nose!

She made such a commotion,
  That little Jenny Wren,
Flew down into the garden,
  And popped it on again!

Little Bo-Peep has lost her sheep,
    And can't tell where
        to find them;
Leave them alone,
    and they'll come home,
Wagging their tails behind them.

Little Bo-Peep fell fast asleep,
And dreamt she heard
        them bleating;
But when she awoke,
    she found it a joke,
For still they all were fleeting.

Then up she took her little crook,
Determined for to find them;
She found them indeed,
        but it made her heart bleed,
For they'd left all their tails
                behind them!

It happened one day,
    as Bo-peep did stray,
Unto a meadow hard by,
There she espied
    their tails side by side,
All hung on a tree to dry.

She heaved a sigh
            and wiped her eye,
And over the hillocks she raced;
And tried what she could,
    as a shepherdess should,
That each tail should
            be properly placed

H ickory Dickory dock,
   The mouse ran up the clock;
The clock struck one,
   the mouse ran down,
Hickory Dickory dock.

See-saw, Margery Daw,
Jack shall have a new master;
He shall have but a penny a day
Because he can't work any faster.

Old Mother Hubbard
went to the cupboard
To give her poor dog a bone,
But when she got there,
the cupboard was bare,
And so the poor dog had none.